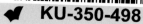

KU-350-498

Mindbending
OPTICAL
ILLUSIONS

Managing Editor: Simon Melhuish
Series Editor: Nikole G. Bamford
Page layout and cover design: Al Shiner

Published by:
LAGOON BOOKS
UK: PO BOX 311, KT2 5QW, UK
US: 10685-B HAZLEHURST DR. #9988, HOUSTON, TX 77043, USA

www.thelagoongroup.com

ISBN 978-1-907780-12-7

© LAGOON BOOKS, 2010

Batch Code: 05 15
Printed in China.

Mindbending
OPTICAL
ILLUSIONS

Other titles in the Mindbending range include:

Mindbending Classic Logic Puzzles

Mindbending Conundrums & Puzzles

Mindbending Lateral Thinking & Puzzles

Mindbending Speed Puzzles

Mindbending Mind Trickery

INTRODUCTION

This book contains a colorful mix of the greatest, most dazzling and visually intriguing of the world's classic optical illusions. Colors, perspective and depth combine to play havoc on your brain; straight lines appear to bend, structures are impossible, shapes spin and colors appear and disappear at will.

So, if you are ready for the ultimate visual challenge; turn over, train your eye and be amazed at the wondrous world of optical illusions!

What do you see first – the face or an eskimo?

Stare at the eye of the magenta parrot while you slowly count to 20,
then immediately look at one spot in the empty birdcage.
The faint, ghostly image of a blue-green bird should appear
in the cage. Try the same thing with the green cardinal,
and a faint magenta bird should appear.

7

Which are the perfect squares?

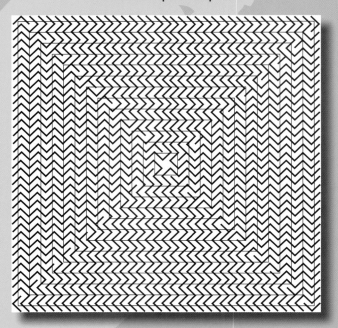

Are you sure?

What do you see first – an old or young man?

What do you see – a rabbit or a duck?

Is this really a square?

What can you see – a vase or faces?

How many legs does this elephant have?

Where are the wavy lines?

Stare at the center of the two gates.
Then, very slowly, bring the page towards your face and see
what happens to the gates.

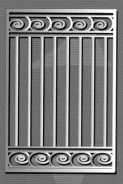 

**Stare at the cross for 60 seconds and then look at a
blank piece of paper. You should see a colored afterglow.**

Is the square really there?

An impossible bar, or is it?
(Turn the book around and look at the bar from every angle.)

Which arc comes from the biggest ellipse?
Can you believe it's the bottom one?

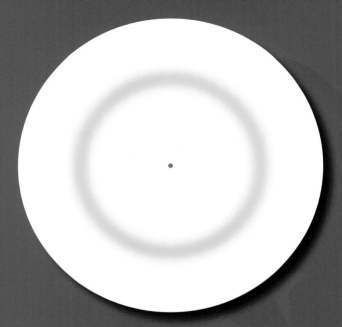

Stare at the center dot and watch the blue circle disappear.

Can you read this text?

Aoccdrnig to rscheearch at Cmabrigde Uinervtisy, it deosn't mttaer in waht oredr the ltteers in a wrod are, the olny iprmoetnt tihng is taht the frist and lsat ltteer be at the rghit pclae. The rset can be a toatl mses and you can sitll raed it wouthit porbelm. Tihs is bcuseae the huamn mnid deos not raed ervey lteter by istlef, but the wrod as a wlohe.

DARK GREEN

LIGHT GREEN

How different are the greens at either end?

I
LOVE
PARIS IN THE
THE SPRINGTIME

Can you find the figure hidden in the picture above?

Do these look like they're moving?

Are you seeing a balustrade or a conversation?

Are you seeing the pulsating lines?

Are these concentric circles?

Do you see a flower, or lots of
concentric circles?

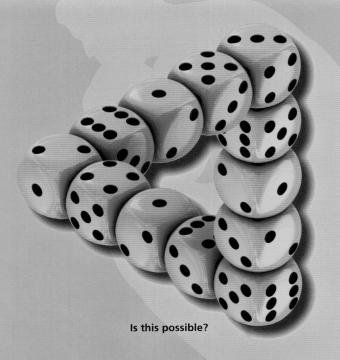

Is this possible?

Is this possible?

A scintillating vortex of shapes.

How many white spots are there?
Or black ones? Or gray ones?

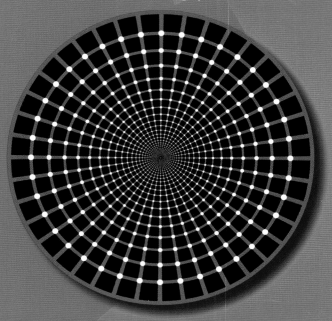

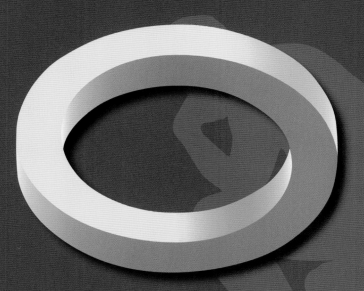

How many surfaces on this ring?

Where do all the staircases lead?

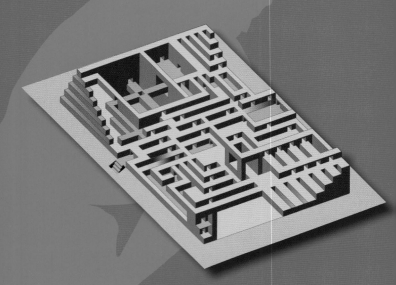

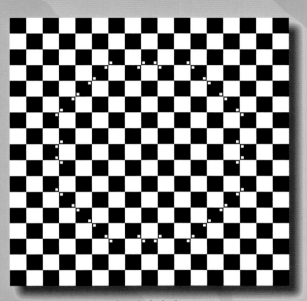

Does this circle bulge out?

Stare at this for a few seconds. Where are the circles going?

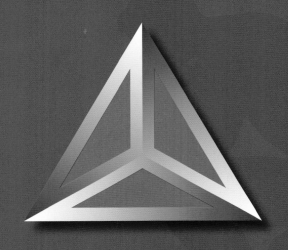

Are you looking down onto the pyramid or are you looking into the pyramid?

Are you caught looking at the top of a hat or into a whirlpool?

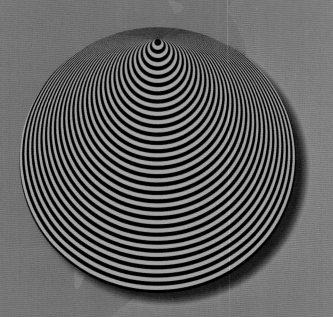

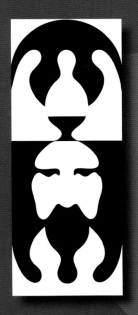

Stare at this image for a few seconds then stare at a blank page.
What do you see?

Don't get dizzy.

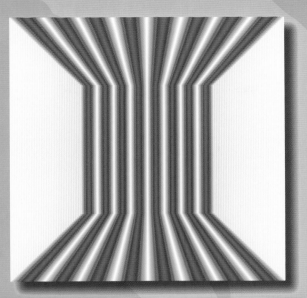

Are you looking into a room?

Are these lines vibrating?

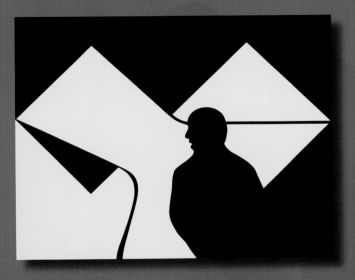

Can you see the half-faced man between the pyramids and the bust of Nefertiti?

Are these really wobbly lines?

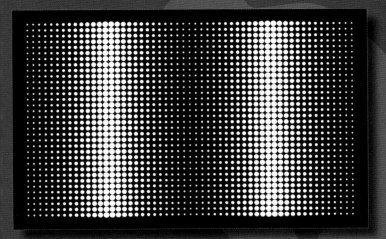

What's spinning?

Are these boxes ascending or descending?

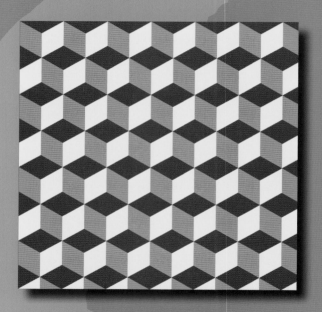

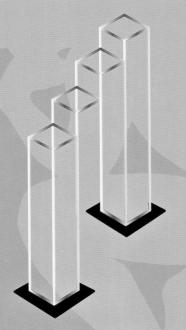

How many bars are there?

Are the lines really wobbly?

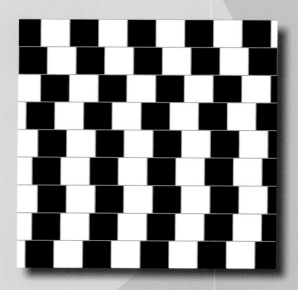

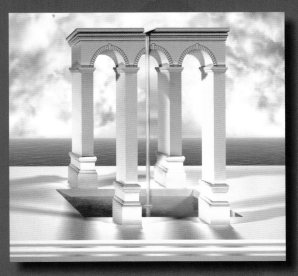

Are these impossible columns?

Are these really spinning?

Where are the squares?

What is the cat actually sitting on?

Is this a real spiral?

What colors do you see at the intersections?

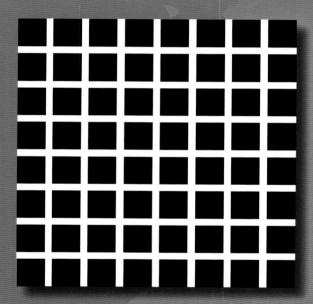

Is this foot an imprint or in relief?

Can you see the circles vibrating?

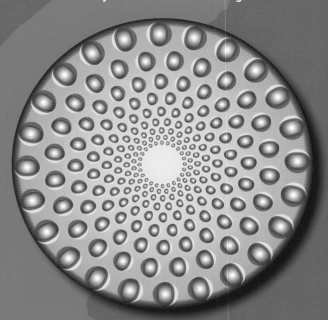

Are the zigzags pulling you in?

**Are you surprised that your
eye is drawn to the smallest tree?**

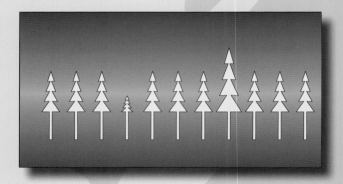

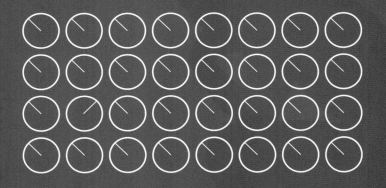

How quickly can you spot the faulty readout?

Is this ring the same gray all the way round?

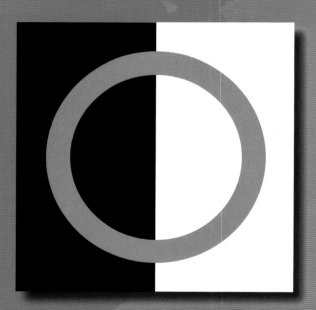

Is this an impossible shelf?

Can you stare at this design without your eyes constantly shifting out of focus?

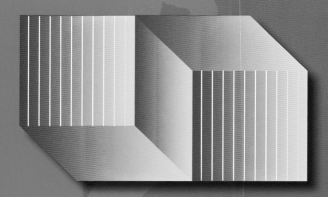

Stare at the pink dots for a few seconds and then look at a blank piece of paper.

Is there more blue or more red?
Neither, they are the same!

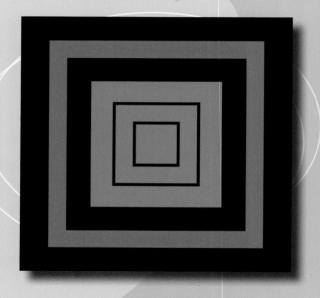

Stare at the light bulb for 60 seconds
and then look at a white piece of paper.
Can you see the light bulb glowing?

What color are the lines and corners?

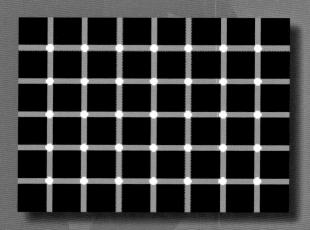

Is the ball nearer the top of the triangle or the bottom?
Neither – it's right in the middle.

How many curved lines in this figure?

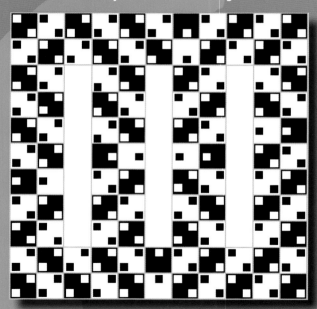

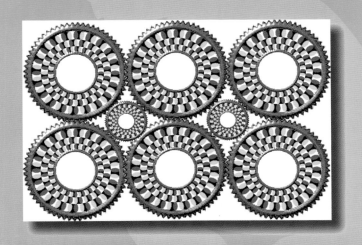

Are these cogs really turning?

An absolute classic – follow the stairs and where do you end up?

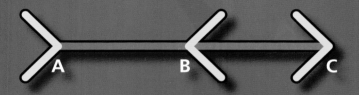

Which is bigger, the line between A and B or B and C?

Can you see the virtual sphere?

Are these balls really on the same level?

Is the top of the lamp shade longer then the top of the lamp base?
If you can't decide, get out a ruler and check!

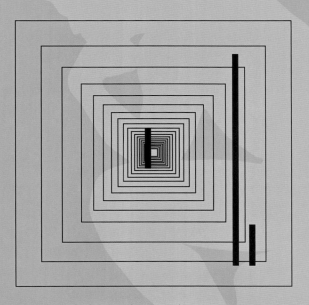

Which line is longer – the one in the center or the one on the right?

Which dot marks the center of the circle?

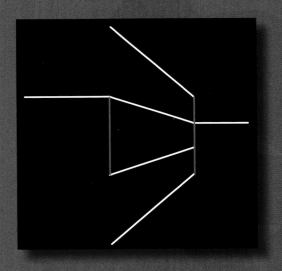

Which red line is longer?

Is the red dot inside or outside?

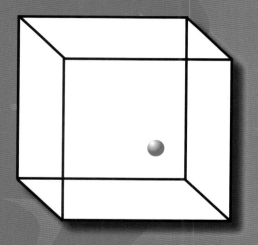

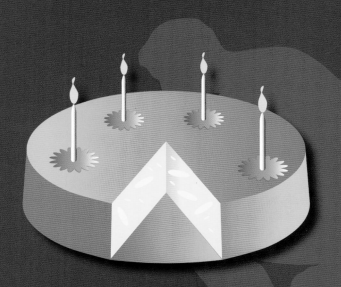

It looks as if a piece of cake is missing, but is it really?

What is the first word you see?

h
i
cyclone
e

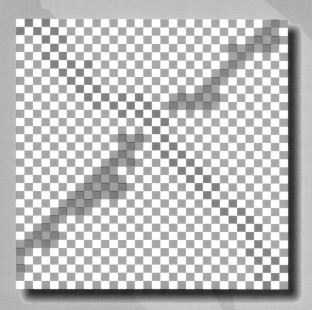

Can you believe there are only two colors in this figure?

Can you read this word?

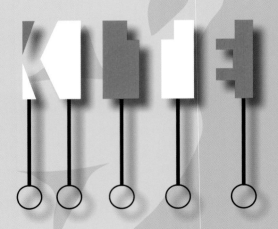

Which wall would you least like to fall off?
It will hurt either way, as they are both the same height!

Look at this picture. Are you looking down on a stack of rings or up a tunnel of rings?

Can you stop these beans from undulating?

**Stare at this for a few seconds, then at a piece of white paper.
What can you see now?**

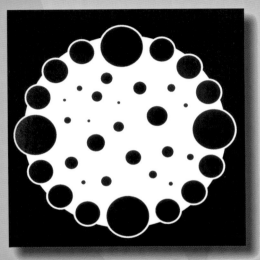

Can you see the white circles flashing?

How different are these orange colors?

Which of the four sections continues the top line?

Can you see diagonal gray lines?

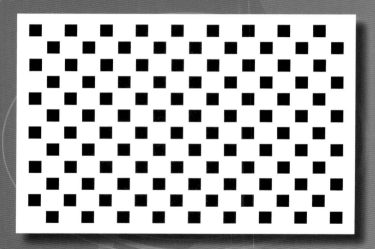

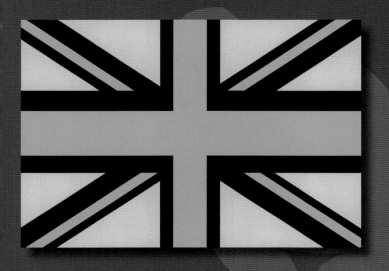

Are these the wrong colors? Stare at the flag for 60 seconds and then look at a white piece of paper. You should see the correct colors in the after-image.